minibumper
b o o k   o f
Love Songs

VOLUME 2

Production: Sadie Cook
Cover design and typesetting by PCD

Published 1997

After The Love Has Gone

Words and Music by DAVID FOSTER,
JAY GRAYDON and BILL CHAMPLIN

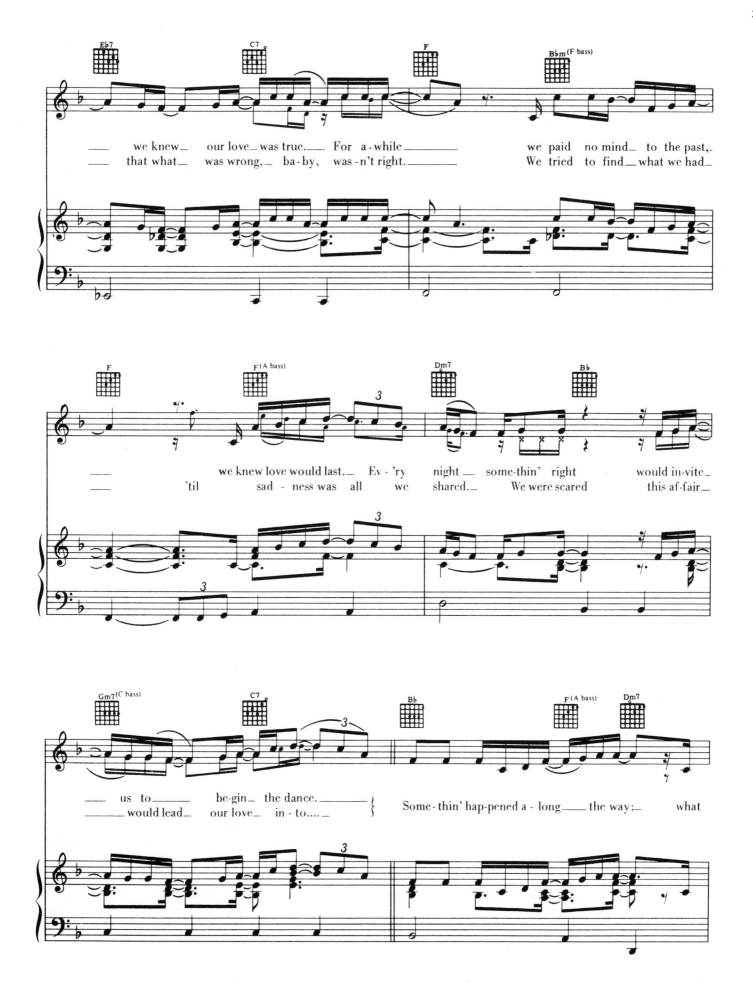

Again

Words and Music by JANET JACKSON,
JAMES HARRIS III and TERRY LEWIS

Always

Words and Music by JOHN LEWIS,
DAVID LEWIS and WAYNE LEWIS

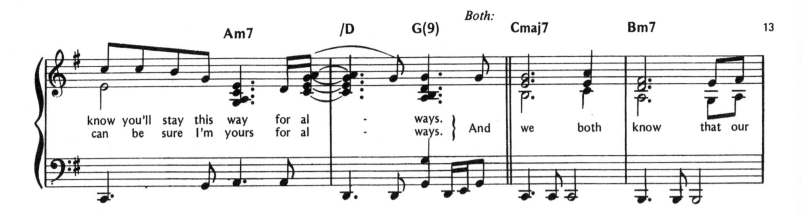

Both:

know you'll stay this way for al - ways.
can be sure I'm yours for al - ways. } And we both know that our

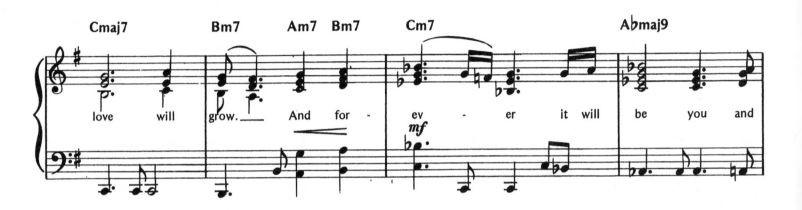

love will grow.____ And for - ev - er it will be you and

Chorus:

me. Ooh, you're like the sun,____ chas-ing all the__rain a-way.

When you come a-round,__ you bring bright - er days.____ You're the per-fect one ____ for me,

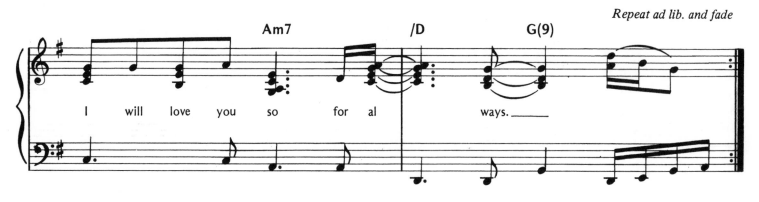

Anything For You

Words and Music by GLORIA ESTEFAN

repeat ad lib. to fade

Baby Come To Me

Words and Music by ROD TEMPERTON

when you're all a-lone.__ Don't talk __ an-y-more, 'cause you

D.S.S. al 2nd ending

know that I'll __ be here to keep you warm. _____ Ba-by,

2. Spendin' ev'ry dime to keep you
Talkin' on the line;
That's how it was, and
All those walks together
Out in any kind of weather,
Just because.
There's a brand new way of
Looking at your life, when you
Know that love is standing by your side.

To Chorus:

Because You Loved Me

Words and Music by DIANE WARREN

Can't Fight This Feeling

Words and Music by KEVIN CRONIN

I can't fight_ this feel - in' an - y - more._____

Careless Whisper

Words and Music by GEORGE MICHÆL
and ANDREW RIDGELEY

40

Forever Love

Words and Music by GARY BARLOW

1. Love it has so ma-ny beau-ti-ful fa-
2.(Instrumental)

-ces, shar-ing lives

Eternal Flame

Words and Music by BILLY STEINBERG,
TOM KELLY and SUSANNA HOFFS

(Everything I Do) I Do It For You

Words and Music by BRYAN ADAMS,
ROBERT JOHN 'MUTT' LANGE and MICHAEL KAMEN

VERSE 2:
Look into your heart
You will find there's nothin' there to hide
Take me as I am, take my life
I would give it all, I would sacrifice.

Don't tell me it's not worth fightin' for
I can't help it, there's nothin' I want more
You know it's true, everything I do
I do it for you.

Get Here

Words and Music by BRENDA RUSSELL

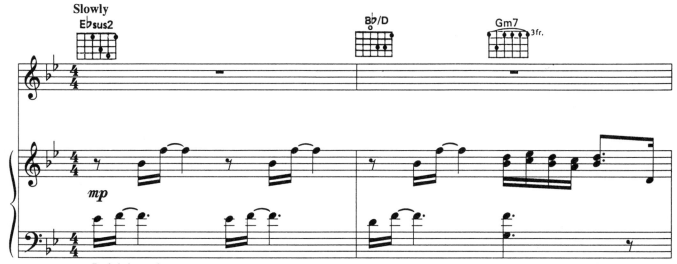

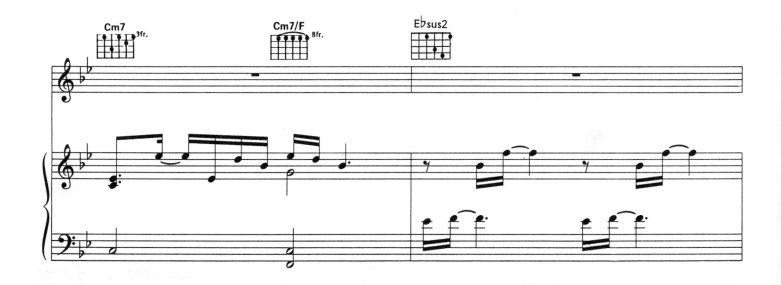

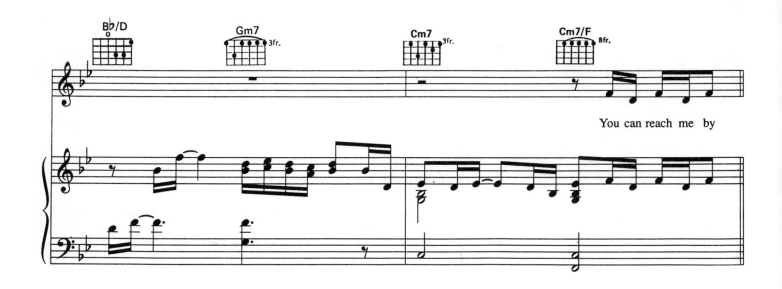

You can reach me by

Goodbye To Love

Words and Music by JOHN BETTIS
and RICHARD CARPENTER

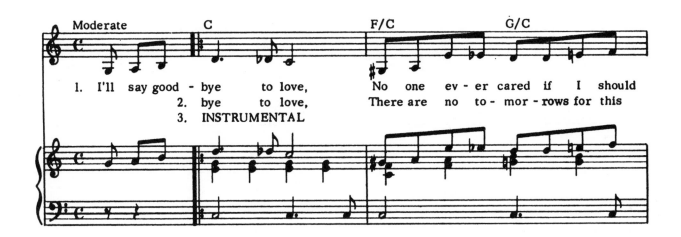

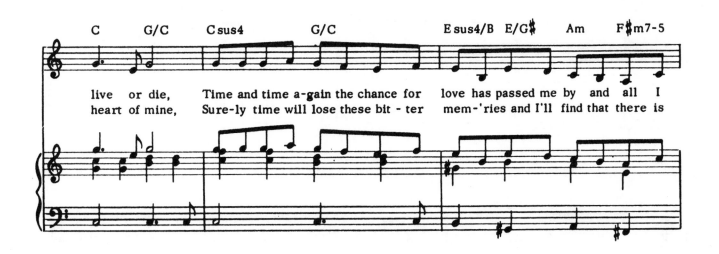

The Greatest Love Of All

Words by LINDA CREED
Music by MICHAEL MASSER

Here We Are

Words and Music by GLORIA ESTEFAN

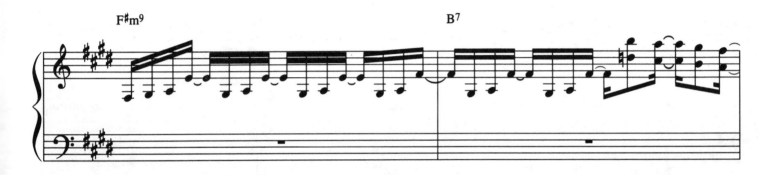

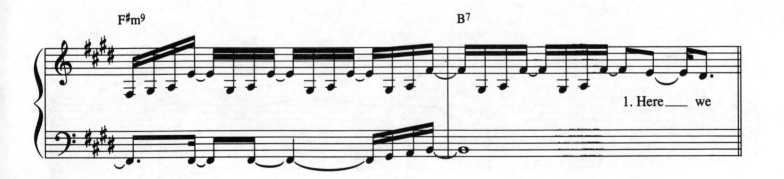

1. Here___ we

Verse 2:

Here we are all alone;
Trembling hearts, beating strong;
Reaching out, a breathless kiss
I never thought could feel like this.
I want to stop the time from passing by.
I want to close my eyes and feel
Your lips are touching mine.
Baby, when you're close to me,
I want you more each time.
And there's nothing I can do
To keep from loving you.

(To Bridge:)

Hero

Words and Music by
WALTER AFANASIEFF and MARIAH CAREY

I Wanna Be Loved By You

Words by BERT KALMAR
Music by HERBERT STOTHART and HARRY RUBY

See page 78 for intro and verse

REFRAIN

INTRODUCTION AND VERSE

How 'Bout Us

Words and Music by DANA WALDEN

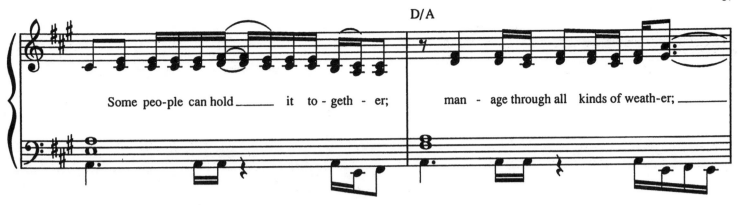

Some peo-ple can hold _____ it to-geth - er; man - age through all kinds of weath-er; _____

_____ can _____ we?_____

we?__ How 'bout us? How 'bout us, ba-by?__

How 'bout us? How 'bout us, ba - by? How 'bout us? How 'bout us, ba - by?

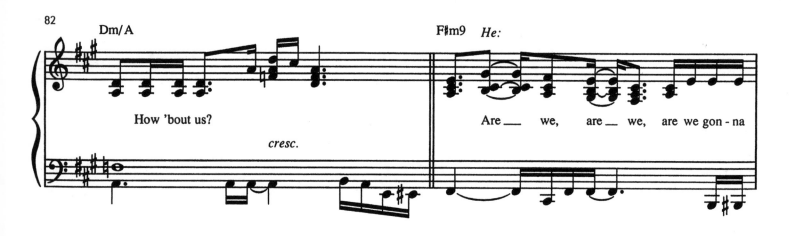

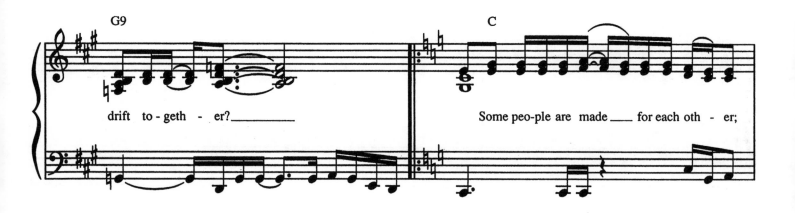

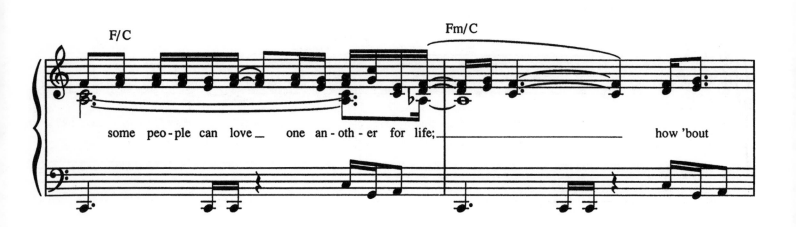

us?_____

Some peo-ple can hold_____ it to - geth - er;

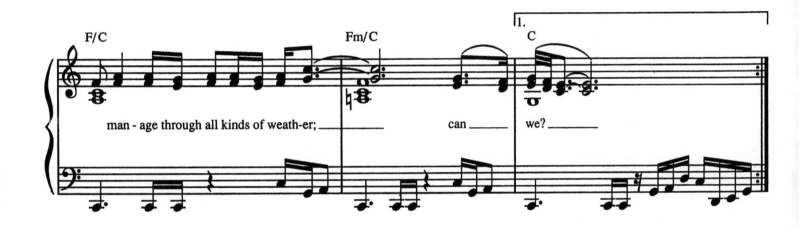

man - age through all kinds of weath-er;_____ can_____ we?_____

2.

we?_____

How 'bout

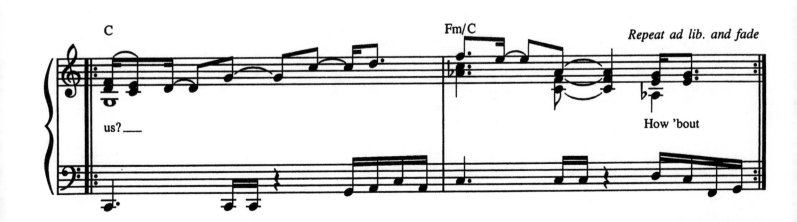

Repeat ad lib. and fade

us?_____

How 'bout

I Swear

Words and Music by
GARY BAKER and FRANK J MYERS

Additional lyrics

2. I'll give you everything I can,
I'll build your dreams with these two hands,
And we'll hang some memories on the wall.
And when there's silver in your hair,
You won't have to ask if I still care,
'Cause as time turns the page my love won't age at all.
(To Chorus)

I Won't Last A Day Without You

Words by PAUL WILLIAMS
Music by ROGER NICHOLS

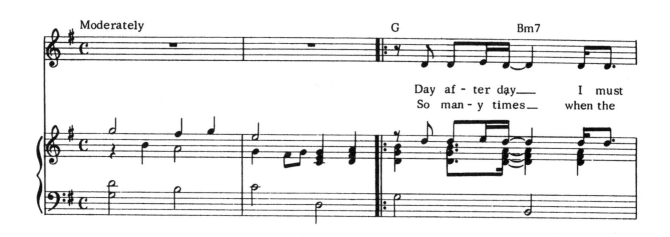

got - ten half their prom - is - es they're not un - kind, just

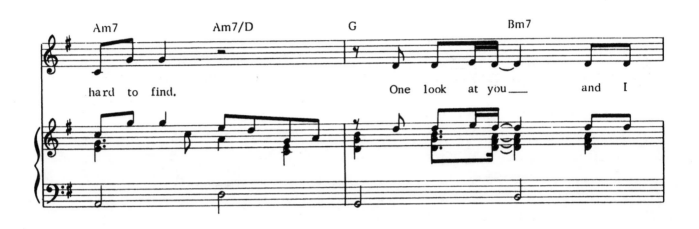

hard to find. One look at you___ and I

know that I___ could learn to live with - out the rest, I

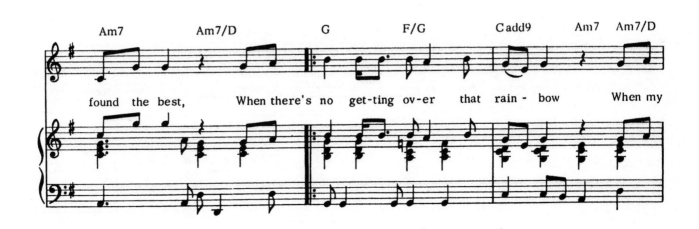

found the best, When there's no get - ting ov - er that rain - bow When my

I Will Always Love You

Words and Music by DOLLY PARTON

Verse 3: Instrumental solo

Verse 4:
I hope life treats you kind
And I hope you have all you've dreamed of.
And I wish to you, joy and happiness.
But above all this, I wish you love.
(To Chorus:)

I'll Be There

Words and Music by BERRY GORDY,
HAL DAVIES, WILLIE HUTCH and BOB WEST

2. I'll reach out my hand to you:
   I'll have faith in all you do.
   Just call my name and I'll be there.

3. Let me fill your heart with joy and laughter.
   Togetherness, girl, is all I'm after:
   Whenever you need me, I'll be there.
   I'll be there to protect you,
   With unselfish love that respects you.
   Just call my name, I'll be there.

Is This Love?

Words and Music by
DAVID COVERDALE and JOHN SYKES

I should have known bet - ter   than to   let you go __ a - lone, __
I   find   I   spend my   time   wait-ing on __ your call, __
I   can't   stop the   feeling I've   been this way __ be - fore, __

it's times   like   these __   I   can't   make it on __ my own,
how can   I   tell you   babe, my   back's a - gainst   the wall.
but with   you I've found the   key   to   op - en a - ny door.

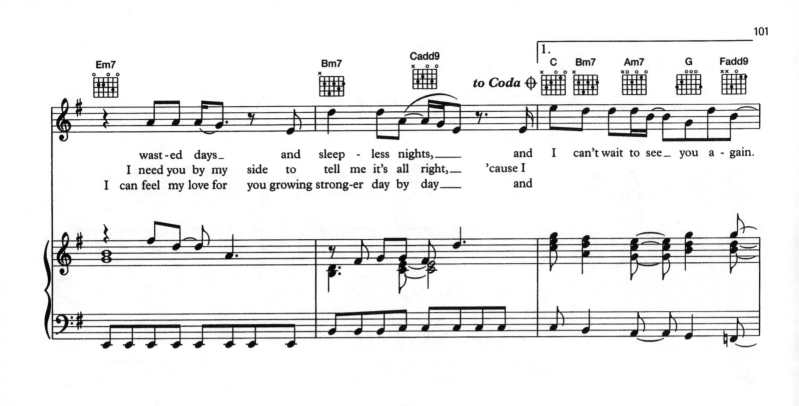

wast-ed days___ and sleep - less nights,___ and I can't wait to see___ you a - gain.
I need you by my side to tell me it's all right,___ 'cause I
I can feel my love for you growing strong-er day by day___ and

don't think I can take a - ny - more.___ Is this love

Chorus

that I'm feel - ing, is this the love___ that I've been

(I've Had) The Time Of My Life

Words and Music by FRANKIE PREVITE,
JOHN DE NICOLA and DONALD MARKOWITZ

Now I've had the time of my life,___ no I ne-ver felt_ this way be-fore, yes I swear it's the truth,___ and I owe it all to you,___ 'cause___ I've had the time of my life___ and I owe it all to you.___

104

love. Be - cause I've ___ had ___ the time of my

life, ___ no I ne - ver felt ___ this way be - fore, yes I

swear it's the truth ___ and I owe it all to you. ___

(2.) With my

Now I've had the time of my life_____ no I ne - ver felt__ this way be -

Just The Two Of Us

Words and Music by RALPH MacDONALD,
WILLIAM SALTER and BILL WITHERS

Verse 2:
We look for love; no time for tears;
Wasted water's all that is, and it don't make no flowers grow.
Good things might come to those who wait,
But not for those who wait too late;
We've got to go for all we know.
Just the ... *(To Chorus:)*

Verse 3:
I hear the crystal raindrops fall on the window down the hall,
And it becomes the morning dew.
And darling, when the morning comes, and I see the morning sun,
I want to be the one with you.
Just the ... *(To Chorus:)*

Just When I Needed You Most

Words and Music by RANDY VAN WARMER

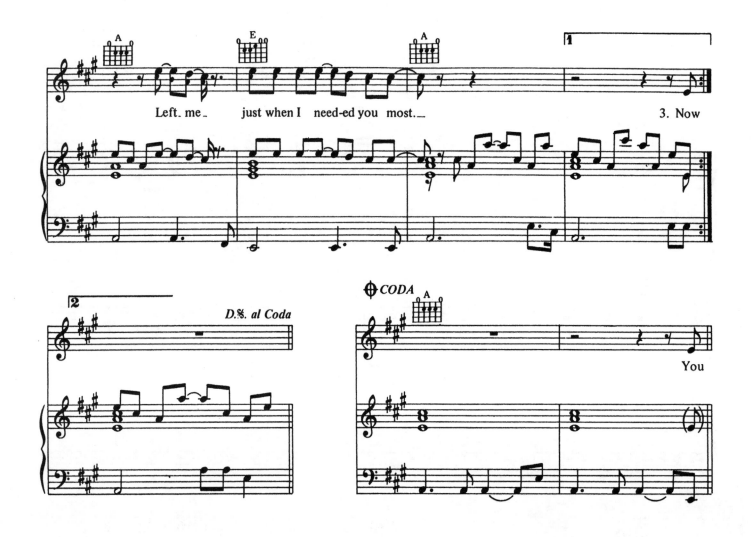

Left. me_ just when I need-ed you most._ 3. Now

D.%. al Coda

⊕ *CODA*

You

Verse 1: Repeat.

Verse 6: Now I love you more than I loved you before,
And now where I'll find comfort, God knows
'Cause you left me, just when I need you most,
Oh yea, you left me, just when I needed you
Most, you left me, just when I needed you most.

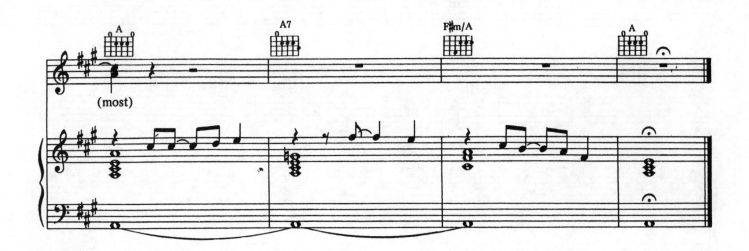

(most)

Killing Me Softly With His Song

Words and Music by
NORMAN GIMBEL and CHARLES FOX

1. I heard__ he   sang__   a   good__ song,   I heard   he   had__
2. I felt__ all   flushed__ with fe - ver,   em - bar - rassed by__
3. He sang__ as   if__   he   knew__ me,   in all   my   dark__

__ a style.
__ the crowd,   And so__   I   came__ to see__ him to
__ des - pair.   I felt__   he   found__ my let - ters and
                  And then__ he   looked__ right through__ me as

The Lady In Red

Words and Music by CHRIS DE BURGH

1. I've nev - er seen you look-ing so love - ly as you did___ to - night,
nev - er seen you look-ing so gor - geous as you did___ to - night,

I've nev - er seen you shine so ___ bright,
I've nev - er seen you shine so ___ bright,

mm mm mm mm.
you were a - maz - ing.

I've
I've

Lately

Words and Music by STEVIE WONDER

Moderately Slow

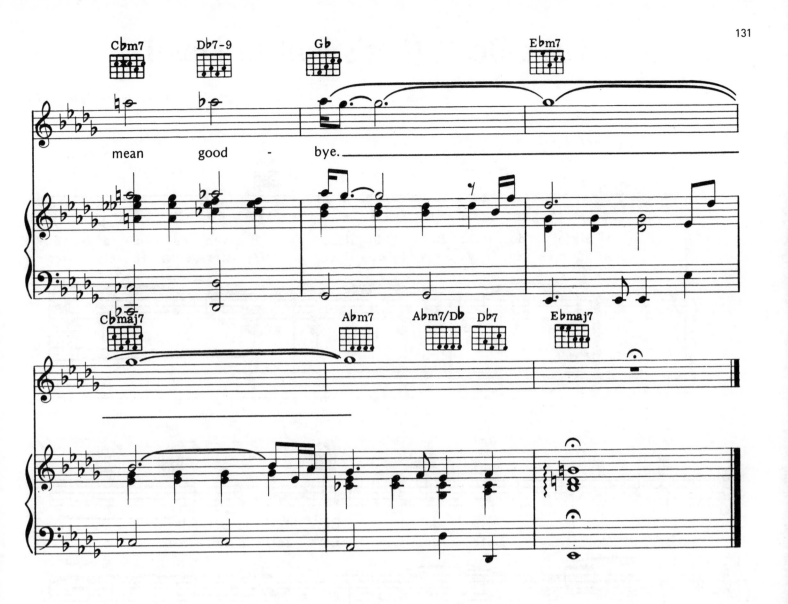

mean good - bye. _____

2nd Verse: Lately I've been staring in the mirror,
Very slowly picking me apart;
Trying to tell myself I have no reason
With your heart.
Just the other night while you were sleeping,
I vaguely heard you whisper someone's name.
But when I ask you of the thoughts you're keeping,
You just say nothing's changed.
Well, I'm a man.........etc.

Let's Do It (Let's Fall In Love)

Words and Music by COLE PORTER

The Most Beautiful Girl In The World

Words and Music by

behind. Cuz baby, this kind of beauty has got no reason 2 be shy, this kind of beauty is the kind that comes from inside.

Could U be _____ the Most Beau - ti - ful Girl _ in the World? _

_ It's plain 2 see, _ U're the rea -

son that God _ made a girl. _ Could U be _

Love Is A Many Splendoured Thing

Words by PAUL FRANCIS WEBSTER
Music by SAMMY FAIN

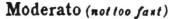

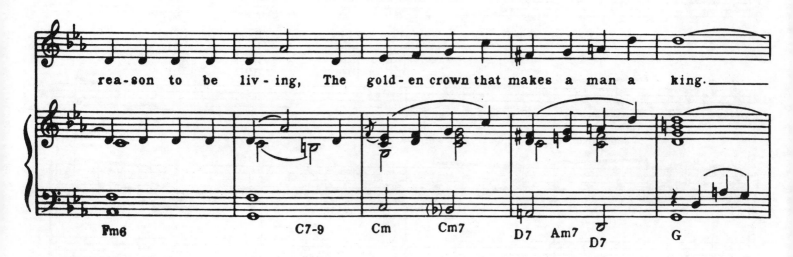

Make It With You

Words and Music by DAVID GATES

A Million Love Songs

Words and Music by GARY BARLOW

VERSE 2:
Looking to the future now, this is what I see,
A million chances pass me by, a million chances to hold you.
Take me back, take me back to where I used to be,
Hide away from all my truths, through the light I see.

CHORUS:
A million love songs later,
Here I am trying to tell you that I care.
A million love songs later,
And here I am, just for you girl;
A million love songs later,
Here I am.

More Than Words

Words and Music by
NUNO BETTENCOURT and GARY CHERONE

more ___ than ___ words. ___

- ing "I ___ love ___ you."

D.S.
Now that I've tried to talk to you
And make you understand
All you have to do is close your eyes
And just reach out your hands
And touch me
Hold me close, don't ever let me go
More than words
Is all I ever needed you to show
Then you wouldn't have to say
That you love me
'Cause I'd already know.

Nobody Does It Better

Words by CAROLE BAYER SAGER
Music by MARVIN HAMLISCH

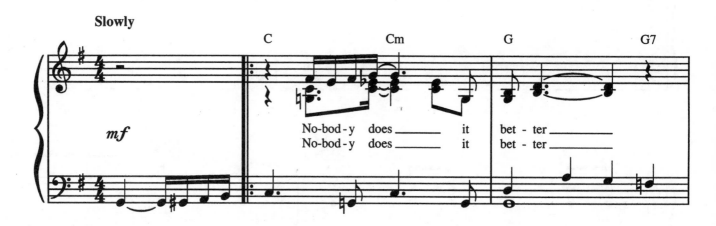

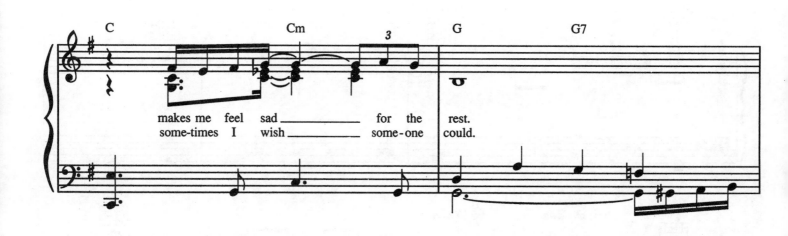

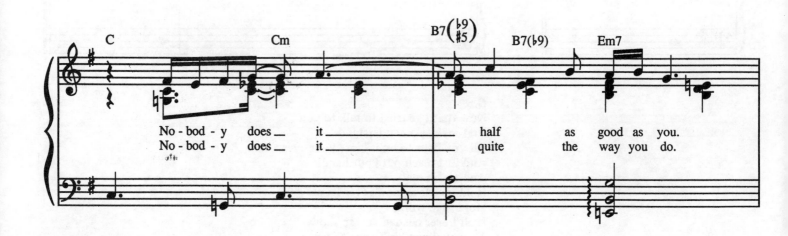

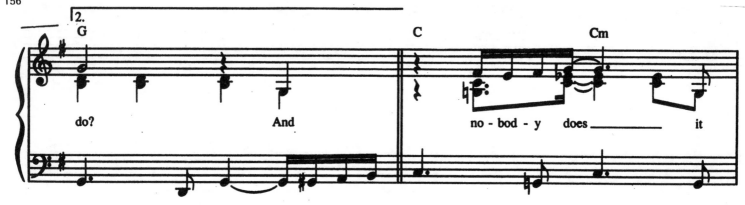

Nothing's Gonna Change My Love For You

Words and Music by
GERRY GOFFIN and MICHAEL MASSER

had   to   live __ my   life ____ with - out __ you   near ____ me, ____   the
If   the   road __ a - head ____ is   not __ so   eas - ____ y, ____   our

Nothing's Gonna Stop Us Now

Words and Music by
ALBERT HAMMOND and DIANE WARREN

Look - ing in your eyes I see __ a par - a - dise, this world __

__ so glad I found you, I'm __ not gon - na lose you, what ev -

__ that I found __ is too good __ to be true. __ Stand - ing here be - side you, want __

er it takes __ I will stay __ here with you. __ Take __ you to the good times, see __

Think Twice

Words and Music by
ANDY HILL and PETE SINGFIELD

Slowly ♩ = 66

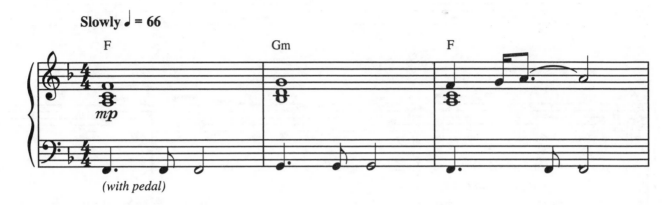

(with pedal)

Verse:

1. Don't think I can't feel that there's some-thing wrong.____

You've been the sweet-est part of__ my life__ for so____ long. I look in your eyes there's a

dis - tant light,____ and you and I know____ there'll be a storm to - night.__

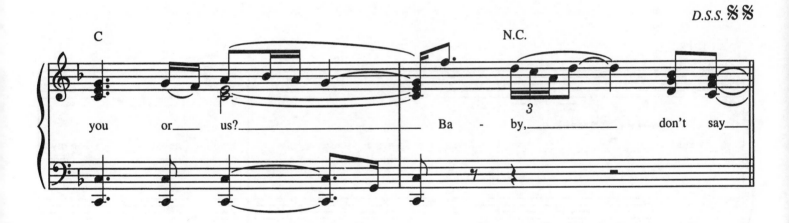

Verse 2:
Baby, think twice for the sake of our love, for the memory,
For the fire and the faith that was you and me.
Baby, I know it ain't easy when your soul cries out for higher ground,
'Cos when you're halfway up, you're always halfway down.
But baby, this is serious.
Are you thinking 'bout you or us?
(To Chorus:)

Chorus 4:
Don't do what you're about to do.
My everything depends on you,
And whatever it takes, I'll sacrifice.
Before you roll those dice,
Baby, think twice.

Now And Forever

Words and Music by RICHARD MARX

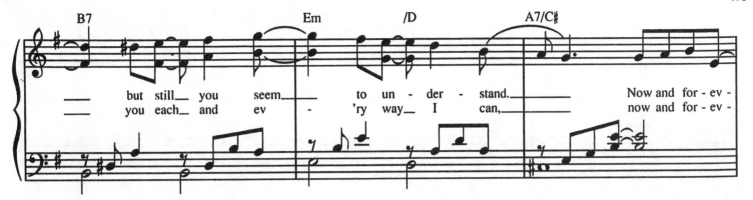

173

If I'd on-ly known___ you were there__ all the time,___ all this time.__

Un-til the day___ the o - cean does - n't touch__ the sand,__

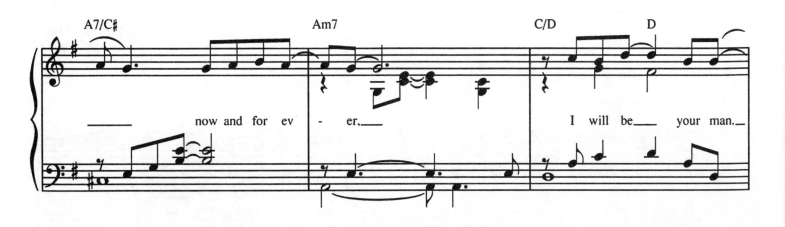

On The Wings Of Love

Words by JEFFREY OSBORNE
Music by PETER SCHLESS

fly – ing high up – on the wings of love,

dim. poco rit.

of

mf   a tempo

love.

molto rit.

Verse 2:
You look at me and I begin to melt
Just like the snow, when a ray of sun is felt.
And I'm crazy 'bout you, baby, can't you see?
I'd be so delighted if you would come with me.
(To Chorus:)

The Rose

Words and Music by
AMANDA McBROOM

love ____ it is a hun - ger ____ an end - less ach - ing

need. ____ I say __ love it is a flow - er ____ and

poco rit. .... *a tempo*

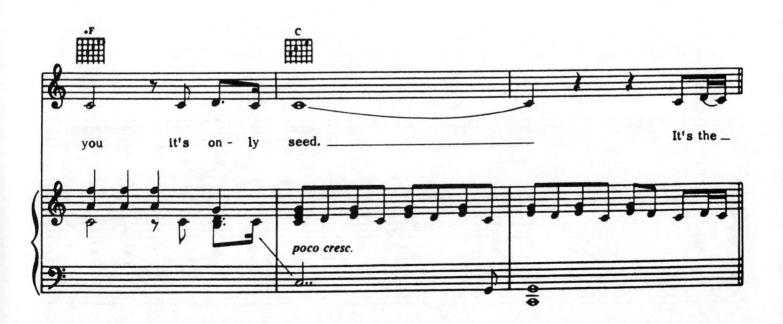

you it's on - ly seed. _____ It's the __

poco cresc.

184

Save The Best For Last

Words and Music by WENDY WALDMAN,
JON LIND and PHIL GALDSTON

Separate Lives

Words and Music by
STEPHEN BISHOP

Chorus 2:

Well, I held on to let you go.
And if you lost your love for me,
You never let it show.
There was no way to compromise.
So now we're living separate lives.

Chorus 3:

You have no right to ask me how I feel.
You have no right to speak to me so kind.
Someday I might find myself looking in your eyes.
But for now, we'll go on living separate lives.
Yes, for now we'll go on living separate lives.

We've Only Just Begun

Words by PAUL WILLIAMS
Music by ROGER NICHOLS

Tryin' To Get The Feeling Again

Words and Music by DAVID POMERANZ

You Are So Beautiful

Words and Music by
BILLY PRESTON and BRUCE FISHER

With You I'm Born Again

Words and Music by
CAROL CONNERS and DAVID SHIRE

soft - ness.___ Com - fort me through all this mad - ness.___

MAN: Wo - man, don't you know with you I'm born a - gain?___
WOMAN: Ly - ing safe with - in your arms, I'm born a - gain.___

Without You

Words and Music by
PETE HAM and TOM EVANS

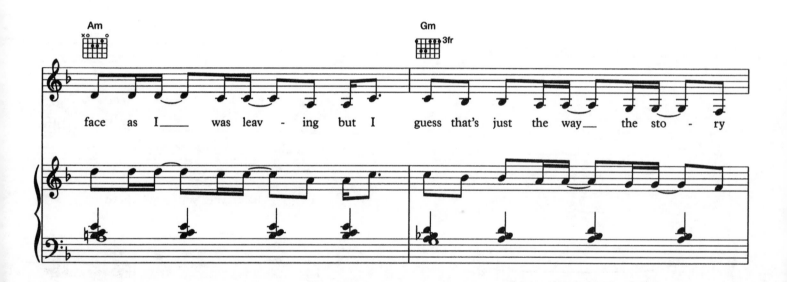

You're The Inspiration

Words and Music by
PETER CETERA and DAVID FOSTER

1. You know our love   was meant to be __
2. *(See additional lyrics)*

the kind of   love __that lasts __for - ev - er. __

And I want you here with   me   from to - night __un - til   the end __

Verse 2:
And I know (yes, I know)
That it's plain to see
We're so in love when we're together.
Now I know (now I know)
That I need you here with me
From tonight until the end of time.
You should know everywhere I go;
Always on my mind, you're in my heart, in my soul.

(To Chorus:)

Printed in Great Britain by Hobbs the Printers Ltd, Totton, Hampshire 1/97